Alphabetical Order

Write the capital letters.

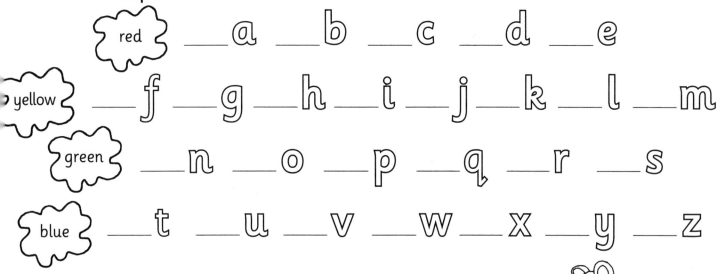

red __ a __ b __ c __ d __ e

yellow __ f __ g __ h __ i __ j __ k __ l __ m

green __ n __ o __ p __ q __ r __ s

blue __ t __ u __ v __ w __ x __ y __ z

Put the words into alphabetical order.

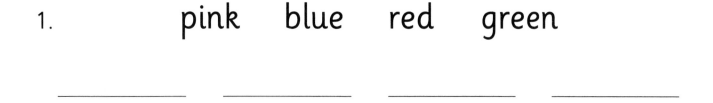

1.   pink   blue   red   green

_____   _____   _____   _____

2.   spotty   fluffy   old   new

_____   _____   _____   _____

3.   hop   skip   jump   run

_____   _____   _____   _____

1

Action: Pretend your finger is a needle and prick your thumb, saying *ou, ou, ou*

Match the words to the pictures.

mountain

house

mouth

mouse

cloud

sprout

Compound Birds

Complete the compound birds.

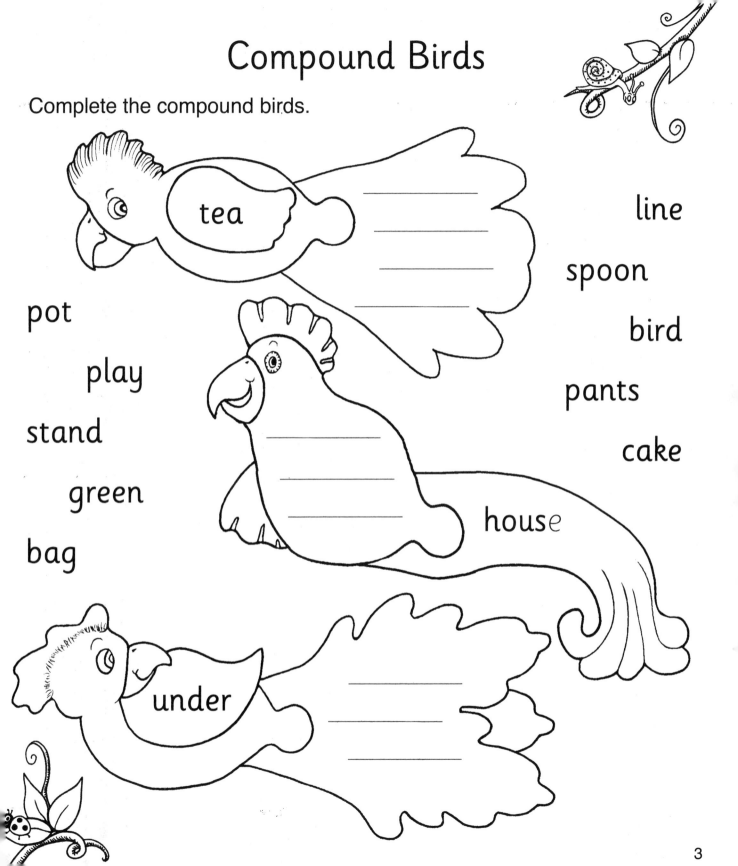

tea _____
_____
_____

line

spoon

pot

play

stand

green

bag

bird

pants

cake

house

under

Using a Dictionary

Using a dictionary, look up the word for each picture. Write the word below the picture and read its meaning.

_____

_____

_____

_____

_____

_____

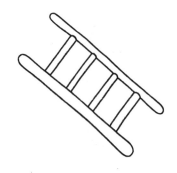

_____

_____

_____

Counting

Colour the numerals and write the numbers underneath.

1

one

2

3

4

5

6

7

8

9

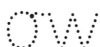 

Look at the pictures and write the words.

_____ _____ _____

_____ _____

Adjectives

 *Blue*

Think of some **adjectives** to describe the flowers and colour them in.

a _____ daisy   a _____ bluebell   a _____ rose

Think of some adjectives to describe the nouns.

a _____ whale   a _____ mouse   a _____ lamp

Remember, **adjectives** are words that describe nouns.

a _____ snowman

7

Verbs  Red

Write three **verbs** and draw Bee doing each one.

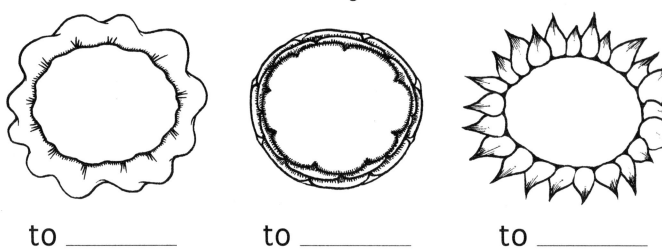

to _____   to _____   to _____

Draw a picture of yourself doing your favourite hobby.

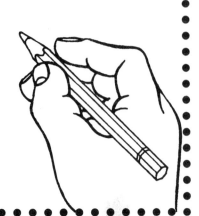

Read the sentences and underline the **verbs** in red.

Red

1. The brown owl <u>flies</u> across the sky.

2. I saw two cows at the farm.

3. They put the seeds in flowerpots.

4. He reads the newspaper.

5. We packed our bags.

6. She shouted very loudly.

7. I made a cup of tea.

8. They played in the snow.

9

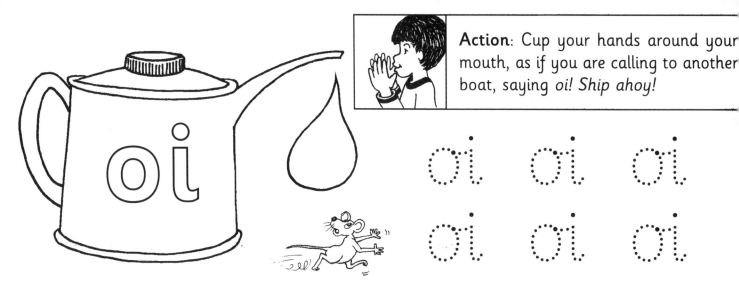

Action: Cup your hands around your mouth, as if you are calling to another boat, saying *oi! Ship ahoy!*

oi oi oi

oi oi oi

Read the words in the oil splodges and draw a picture for each one.

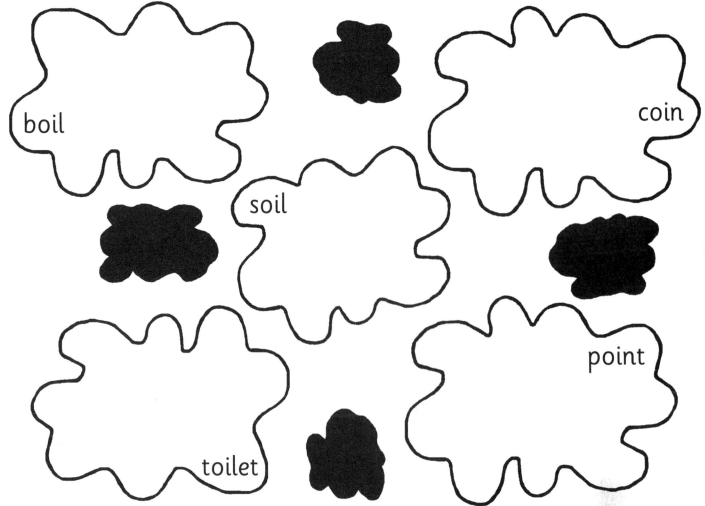

boil

coin

soil

point

toilet

10

 Verbs Red

Write the sentences in the past tense and in the future.

 The owl hoots in the dark.

 The_____.

 The_____.

 She hums the tune.

 She_____.

She_____.

 They enjoy the show.

 They_____.

They_____.

Adverbs

Adverbs are words that describe verbs. If you are not sure how to spell a word, remember to use a dictionary.

Underline the **verbs** in red and the **adverbs** in orange.

Red   *Orange*

1. They <u>sang</u> <u>loudly</u>.

2. The bulb grew rapidly.

3. She played happily.

4. I whispered quietly.

5. He smiled widely.

6. The sun blazed brightly.

 Action: Bang one fist on top of the other.

12

Read the adverbs.

quickly   messily   happily   softly

angrily   sadly   strongly   loudly

Choose an **adverb** to add to each sentence and draw a picture for each one.

Bee cried _____ .	The fish swam _____ .
They clapped _____ .	The bug wiggled _____ .

Action: Cup your hands around your mouth, as if you are calling to another boat, saying *oi! Ship ahoy!*

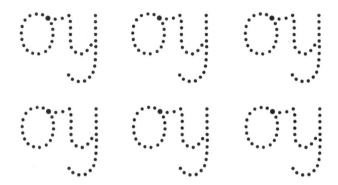

Read the words and draw a picture for each one.

boy	joy	royal	destroy

Draw a picture of your favourite toy.

14

Write some sentences about your favourite toy.

_____

_____

_____

_____

_____

_____

Read the words and draw a picture to illustrate each one.

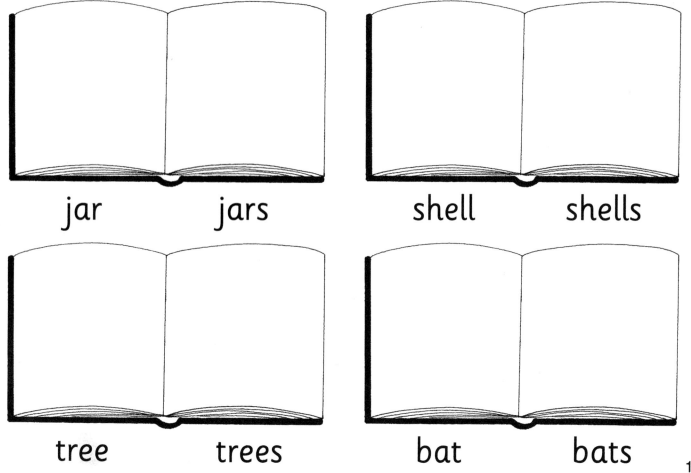

| jar | jars | shell | shells |

| tree | trees | bat | bats |

15

Final Consonant Blends

Sort the words according to their final blends.

elf	elm	yelp	film	gulp	bolt
self	fact	help	melt	bulk	insect
silk	elk	golf	act	belt	kilt

Write the Words

Look at the pictures and write the words.

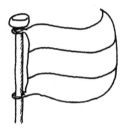

_____   _____   _____

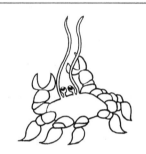

_____   _____   _____

_____   _____   _____

Read the consonant blends.

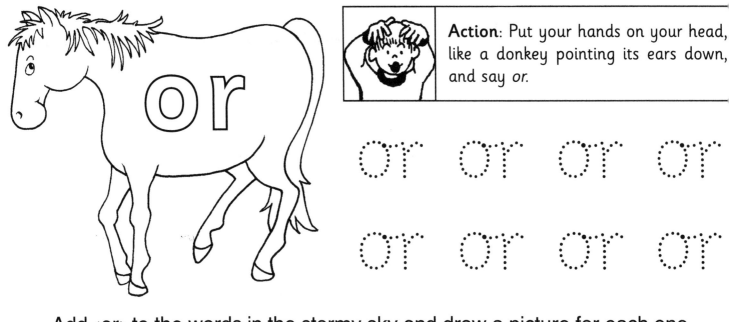

or or or or

or or or or

Add ‹or› to the words in the stormy sky and draw a picture for each one.

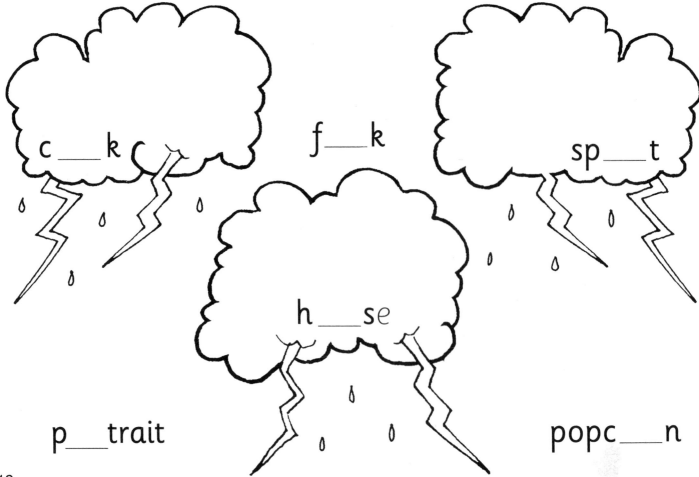

c __ k

f __ k

sp __ t

h __ se

p __ trait

popc __ n

18

'A' or 'An'?

Add 'a' or 'an' to the words. Remember, 'an' is used before a noun that starts with a vowel sound.

_a_ fork

_____ ark

_____ coin

_____ oak tree

_____ mouth

_____ flower

_____ bucket

_____ owl

_____ ant

Plurals

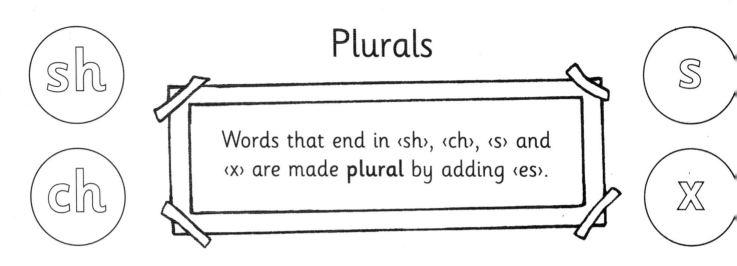

Words that end in ‹sh›, ‹ch›, ‹s› and ‹x› are made **plural** by adding ‹es›.

Make the words plural and draw a picture for each one.

lunch   lunches

fox   _____

dish   _____

bus   _____

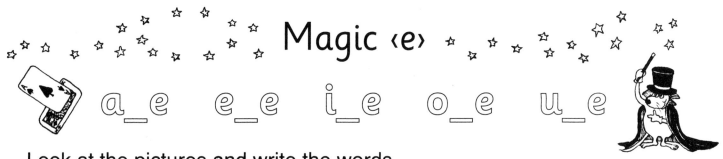

Magic ‹e›

a_e   e_e   i_e   o_e   u_e

Look at the pictures and write the words.

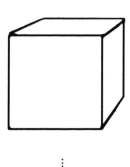

cube
_____

_____

_____

_____

_____

_____

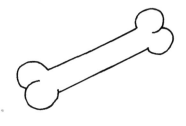

_____

_____

_____

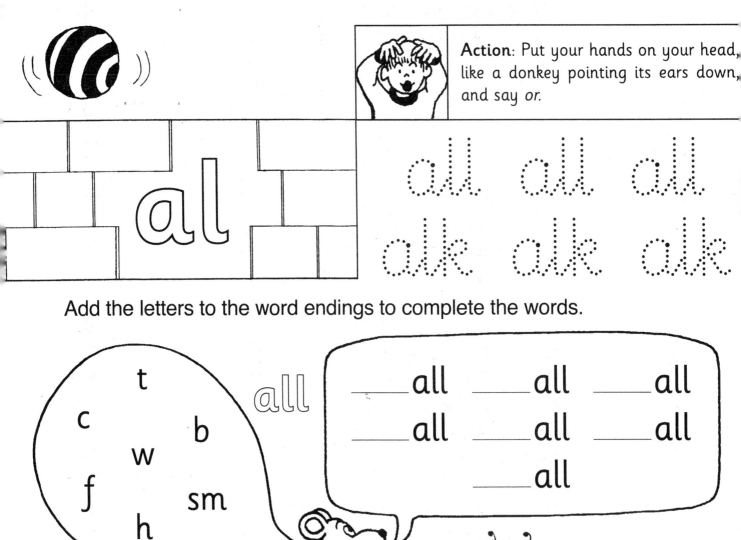

Action: Put your hands on your head, like a donkey pointing its ears down, and say *or*.

all all all
alk alk alk

Add the letters to the word endings to complete the words.

t
c
w b
f sm
h

all

___all ___all ___all
___all ___all ___all
___all

___alk ___alk
___alk ___alk

st
ch
w
t

Antonyms

Write the opposite of each word.

quiet

stop

whisper

little

smile

bad

Write the opposite of each word and draw a picture for each one.

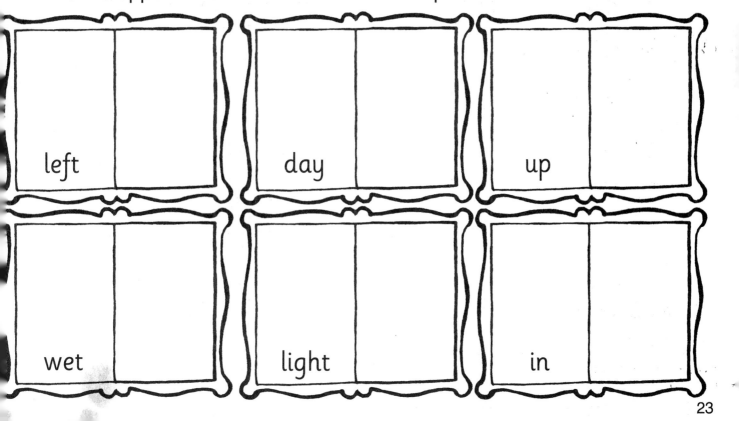

left

day

up

wet

light

in

Tricky Words

Write over the dotted words in the tricky word flowers. Then decorate the page with colourful bugs.